Shakespeare on Stage

Andrew Brownfoot

CW01020642

O! for a Muse of fire, tha
The brightest heaven of i
A kingdom for a stage, princes to act
And monarchs to behold the swelling scene!
... Can this cockpit hold
The vasty fields of France? or may we cram
Within this wooden O the very casques
That did affright the air at Agincourt?

Henry V Chorus

Shakespeare is probably the most gifted playwright in any language that the world has ever known. He was born in 1564 at Stratford-upon-Avon and died in 1616, leaving behind a legacy of wonderful plays that have been performed ever since. Little is known about his life and this has given plenty of opportunity for speculation that the plays were in fact written by someone else. However it is the plays which have survived and which are the lasting memorial. This book explores how they have been treated and staged over the past four hundred years.

As part of this exploration, there are four three-dimensional pull-up theatre scenes to cut out and make. They are presented in the form of personal diaries and tell of the experiences of four theatre-goers in widely different periods of the past. They tell us how they looked forward to the performance of the chosen play and we can read their comments afterwards. Although our diarists are imaginary, they do give us an intriguing insight into what the theatre was like at those times and how Shakespeare was regarded by his audiences.

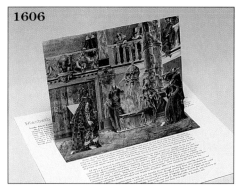

Macbeth at the Globe

1606

Hamlet at the Countess's

1698

Romeo and Juliet at Her Majesty's

1888

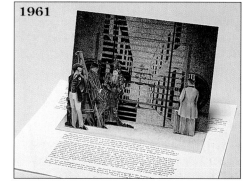

Measure for Measure at St. Martin's

1961

The Globe in Shakespeare's Time

The first public playhouses in London were built on the plan already used for the entertainment of 'bear baiting', a 'sport' which satisfied the blood lust of the average Elizabethan in much the same way as horror films delight many audiences today. The plan could vary in shape from rectangular to multi angled, like the Globe Theatre itself, with two or more galleries for spectators to see the show. Where the unfortunate bears had been tethered and then torn to shreds by mastiffs, a platform stage for the actors was erected. With no fearsome animals in the yard, the space which remained was used for those in the audience who were prepared to stand and thus pay less to see the play. To enter the 'Yard' cost a penny, the 'Galleries' cost two pence and the 'Lords' Rooms' at six pence were for the most extravagant, being closest to the stage and partitioned off from the Galleries.

The stage, about 1.5 metres high, could be as much as 12 metres across and extended into the middle of the Yard. At the back there were two or three entrances for the actors. At the First Gallery level on the 'Tiring Room' facade there was a balcony, sometimes used in the performance but often used for members of the audience. To protect the actors and their expensive costumes from bad weather, a canopy called 'The Heavens' extended over the stage. Actors or objects could be lowered on to the stage from one or more 'huts' on the roof. Thunder effects were also produced there by rolling a stone ball across it. The decoration of the theatre and stage was sumptuous, with carved woodwork that was gilded and painted to look like marble, in the Italian style. The Heavens were painted with sun, moon and stars and perhaps the signs of the zodiac, hangings covered part of the tiring-house facade and green rushes were strewn on the stage itself.

Like all back stage areas, the 'Tiring Room' where the actors 'attired' or dressed for the performance, was a busy crowded and unglamorous space. It smelt of sweat and make-up and, to the outsider, would appear totally chaotic; everyone rushing about and nervously adjusting their wigs, skirts or swords, grabbing a bite to eat, exercising their voices or practising moves.

With no scenery to show where the action was taking place, the actors relied on their powers of declamation and posture. Dressed in lavish costume, they were able to use direct physical contact with the crowd to draw the whole audience into the events they had come to witness. Certain conventions were used to help the audience understand the movements involved in the plot. Entrances and exits were logically planned, so that if a character came on to the stage using the entrance on the left and he was to continue his journey, he would exit using the right hand doorway. If, on the other hand he was to return home, then he would go back through the doorway on the left.

The positions and scale of the three openings on to the stage also had useful symbolic connotations, the two smaller doors on left and right of the stage were the most used, and especially denoted informal locations such as private rooms, the doors of cottages or private town houses or, simply the street or a country path. The larger opening in the centre of the stage was reserved for the formal entrance for kings and princes, otherwise it could be used to introduce or 'discover' a large prop such as a royal throne, a bed or a ship etc. Other entrances were available for special effects. The balcony above the three doors in the tiring house wall was used in a similar fashion. Actors appeared at the sides for informal occasions like Juliet's balcony or in the centre, on formal occasions such as the parlay between King Henry V and the Governor of Harfleur, who appears on the city walls above the gates of the town. The ghost in **Hamlet** stalked the battlements of Elsinore using this same balcony, even though aristocratic members of the audience may well have been sitting there. Trap doors in the stage could be opened for 'prisoners' to be taken to, or brought from, the 'dungeons' and more spectacular magical arrivals could be achieved using them, such as spirits and demons ascending amongst clouds of smoke. As I have already said, gods and celestial beings were lowered from openings in the wooden ceiling of the 'The Heavens'.

3

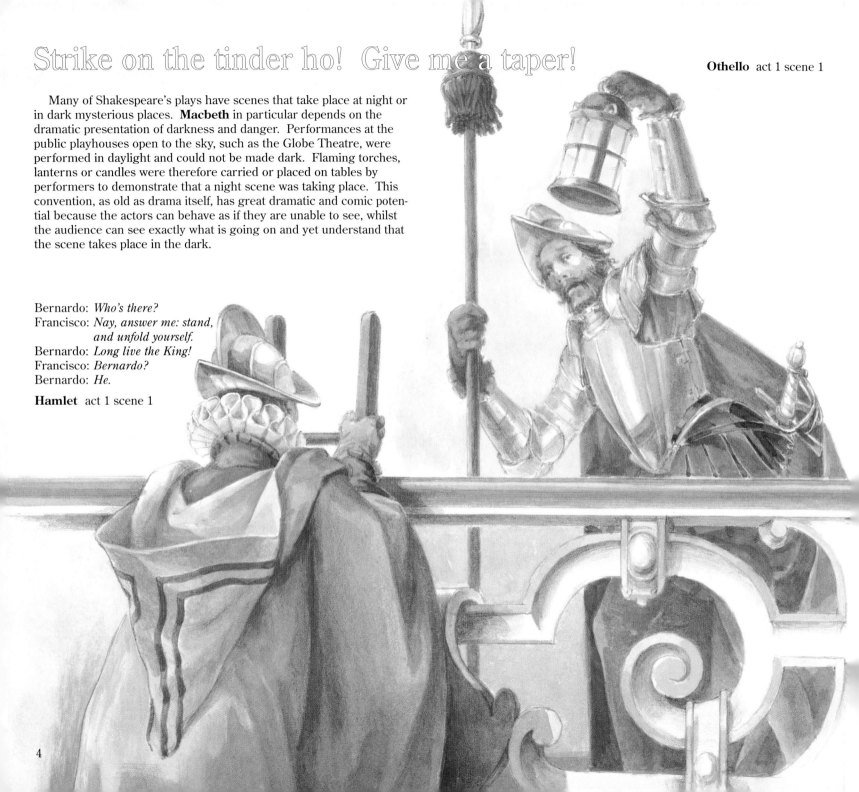

Strike on the tinder ho! Give me a taper!

Othello act 1 scene 1

Many of Shakespeare's plays have scenes that take place at night or in dark mysterious places. **Macbeth** in particular depends on the dramatic presentation of darkness and danger. Performances at the public playhouses open to the sky, such as the Globe Theatre, were performed in daylight and could not be made dark. Flaming torches, lanterns or candles were therefore carried or placed on tables by performers to demonstrate that a night scene was taking place. This convention, as old as drama itself, has great dramatic and comic potential because the actors can behave as if they are unable to see, whilst the audience can see exactly what is going on and yet understand that the scene takes place in the dark.

Bernardo: *Who's there?*
Francisco: *Nay, answer me: stand,*
         and unfold yourself.
Bernardo: *Long live the King!*
Francisco: *Bernardo?*
Bernardo: *He.*

Hamlet act 1 scene 1

4

Lady Alice Conhem's Journal, September 1606

My Lord Goodworth's advice, not to cross over the river to the Globe Theatre is to be ignored this very afternoon! Poor man, he is always so beset with fears and forebodings, he would have me cooped up like a Turk's wife. The play is to be 'Macbeth - his tyrannical and murderous usurpation: with the whole course of his devil-possessed life and most deserved death' or so it is proclaimed. It hath been lately acted before the king and is now to be performed in the playhouse, newly reopened after the plague closing. Lord Goodworth tells me it is most fearful, full of witchcraft and bloody deeds. T'will be a perfect play for us three merry widows!

Lady Strange, Mistress Longjade and I will go, masked, to the play together and thus hope to avoid censure from the malicious gossip that usually attends unaccompanied gentlewomen who go abroad to such places. Lord Goodworth has arranged that we have the use of a gentleman's rooms although he will not join us. This, he says, will at least save us from rough spirits in the yard or the galleries. I will leave writing further as I hear my two sweet gossips have come below. The sun shines though thunder threatens, may the fates protect our linen bands and silken gowns on this adventure! My gossips call for me.

The cut-out pieces for this scene are on page 45. The instructions on how to assemble it are on page 44.

This area glues to page 7

This page becomes the base of a three-dimensional pop-up scene telling the story of a visit to the Globe Theatre in 1606 by Lady Alice Conhem and her friends. To create it:

1. Remove page 5 completely from the book by cutting along the solid line.
2. Cut out the T-shaped piece precisely by cutting around the solid outline.
3. Score along the dotted line and fold it towards you to make a valley fold. Crease firmly to make a hinged flap.
4. Check that the top of the T fits over this grey shaded area and that the hinged flap covers the text beneath. Then glue this flap carefully into position. It then forms the backdrop for the theatre scene.
5. The remaining pieces to complete this scene are on page 45 and the detailed instructions are given on page 44.

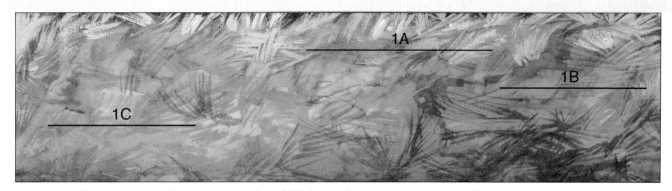

Home at last, and so to my narrative. Midnight is fast upon us and my candle gutters. Macbeth is truly terrible - diabolical effects, unnatural cruelties and death all presented with the greatest discretion, nothing overdone yet so keenly mirrored to nature.   At first we jested that we three widows were well matched with the three witches in the play but the power of the words and the acting performance soon dispelled our mirth and we fell silent and absorbed, feeling in turn, pity, loathing, triumph and despair!

All this was marred by some swaggering fantastical fellows who barred our passage to the room reserved for us and we were forced to sit in the galleries. We found ourselves sitting next to my Lord Downing, whose passage had been blocked by another 'Gallant'. This bully then climbed on to the stage platform and obstinately stood there, blocking our view and with foolish talk that he mistook for wit, provoked a brawl. Lord Downing, losing all patience, threw his half eaten pippin at the arrogant obstacle to our enjoyment. This wastrel then drew his sword and leapt from the platform shouting 'tis but card and paste that afrights your wanton jades, you dullards!' Lord Downing dealt him a blow that, combined with the surfeit of bottled beer drunk by the fellow, and to the delight of all, laid him low.

The uproar only eased when a clap of real thunder accompanied the magical conjuring of the second apparition to answer Macbeth - a piteous bloody child that, though seeming dead, did command 'be bloody, bold and resolute.' Oh I would have swound for as the child said that none of woman born could harm Macbeth, a great flash of lightning, followed by a crash of thunder made it seem that hell itself would burst upon the stage. Macbeth is slain at the end and by Macduff who, we learn, was not born at all but ripped untimely from his mother's womb. I will not sleep this night! It thunders still.

Romeo and Juliet prologue

There is a certain amount of controversy about the length of time needed to perform Shakespeare's plays, that comes from Shakespeare himself. In the prologue to **Romeo and Juliet** he talks of the story being told in the space of two hours. Nowadays the plays take two and a half to three hours to perform. How can this be? One suggestion has been that the actors talked faster than we do today in which case, were the dramatic pauses shorter or their movements across the stage more rapid? The Elizabethans loved poetry and surely would have taken time to savour the richness of Shakespeare's language.

Many of the plays we now read and perform were rescued from oblivion after Shakespeare's death. He had never really concerned himself about publishing his texts. Shakespeare's friends retrieved the well worn manuscripts from the King's Men's storage trunks. Some were Shakespeare's originals, others were fair copies and from these and other remembrances the plays were published. Hemming and Condell were rightly concerned to preserve everything Shakespeare had written. In rehearsal for performance, however, Shakespeare would have altered scenes to fit the time limits imposed by the requirements for a performance at court or for the public playhouse. If two hours was the requirement then the play would be made to fit two hours. Without Shakespeare's presence in life and with his almost god-like reputation amongst today's audience, it takes a brave soul to tamper with these texts; there are some who dare but it is likely that we see more of the plays than Shakespeare's own audiences ever did.

Clocks and watches in Shakespeare's time were comparatively poor timekeepers with only an hour hand to show the time. It was not until the invention of the pendulum by Christian Huygens, in 1657, that sufficient accuracy was achieved to justify a minute hand. A time conscious person looking up at the church clock or, if he was wealthy enough, at his own tiny watch face, would find it difficult to be absolutely precise about the minutes between the hours and usually a bell would strike the hour, the half hour and sometimes the quarter hour. This tolling of the hour is used with great dramatic effect by Shakespeare in **Julius Caesar**. Incidentally the name Clock comes from the vulgar Latin Cloca meaning bell and the first clocks had no face at all. The excessive cost of portable clocks and watches in Shakespeare's time meant that only the very wealthiest could afford them. Most people were happy enough with a pocket sundial and these continued to be used by ordinary folk, well into the 18th century.

Pocket sundials usually had a magnetic compass built in so that they could be aligned to the correct north-south line. Jaques may well have mimed the twisting and turning of the fool (the court jester) telling the time - an extra twist and an hour seems to have passed.

Jacques: *And then he drew a dial from his poke,*
And looking on it, with lack-lustre eye,
Says, very wisely, 'It is ten o'clock: ...'

As You Like It act 2 scene 7

8

On special occasions, especially at Christmas and for the New Year celebrations, Shakespeare's company was called upon to perform for Queen Elizabeth and later, King James and his guests at Court. A stage was erected at one end of the great hall of a palace and, following the latest fashions from Italy, scenery was introduced, including a proscenium arch to provide a formal frame to the action. It hid the rough outer edges of the set and also the performers waiting to make their entrances. The designer's theatre had arrived! Although this innovation cut off the actors from the audience and reduced their involvement, this disadvantage was to some extent overcome by the use of stairs from the stage into the auditorium. Performers could enter or exit through the audience and frequently did.

It seems strange to us now, but at the time, the King and Queen sat centrally on thrones in splendid isolation and at some distance from the stage. No one could sit near the King and Queen and certainly not directly in front of them. The intervening space was therefore large enough to allow additional pieces of scenery to be placed either side of the hall and for groups of dancers to perform on the floor in front of the stage and so avoid the undesirable noise of their feet drumming on the temporary stage platform. The courtiers were arranged round the side and at the back of the room. Ladies' farthingales, tight lacing and gentlemen's bombasted trousers took up a great deal of space and made sitting difficult in these confined conditions. However, standing for hours on end in the royal presence was an accepted part of the courtier's life.

Timeless, but of his time

Although it is often said that Shakespeare never lets us know his own moral sympathies, surely we must assume that the attitudes expressed in his plays must have been acceptable to him and to his audiences. He needed to fill the public playhouses and also to earn the approval of the Court at the time. Although his plays contain ideas and attitudes that would be totally unacceptable in a new play written today, we find ourselves able to empathise with the characters he so powerfully portrays and we still find ourselves laughing at situations which would shock us or shame us if they were set in our own time.

To the snobbish courtier of the period, it seemed perfectly natural to laugh at the ignorance and clumsiness of the uneducated poor and time after time Shakespeare indulges his fashionable audience in this respect. Seldom was it thought possible for a person of low class to be capable of true dignity; when they try to be taken seriously Shakespeare makes them use inappropriate words and we laugh at every mistake they make.

Quince: *Yes and he is the best person too; and he is a very paramour for a sweet voice.*

Flute: *You must say 'paragon': a paramour is, God bless us, a thing of nought*

A Midsummer Night's Dream   act 4 scene 2

Without doubt, such interchanges were good 'box office' at the time and contrasted 'rude mechanicals' who wanted to do things correctly but did not know how, with the sophistication of the court. When produced today, it is common to contrast the regional accents of the tradesmen with the standard English accents of the Court.

Another recurring theme which would jar today, if we were not willing to be transposed to another era, lies in the treatment of women. With a very few exceptions, women in the early 17th century were considered the property of, first their fathers and after marriage, their husbands. Only when she was widowed did a woman have any real independence. In the plays, the most common situation for a cruel injustice is the accusation that she has not been chaste. Unfounded or not, she is cast out, cursed and held up to public dishonour by her father, husband or fiancé. No-one bothers to examine the truth of the accusation before inflicting terrible mental cruelty upon her. Yet, when the truth of her virtue is finally accepted, she still gratefully accepts her subservient condition and happily bows to her 'lord's' will. Few women in our western societies today would behave in the same way and one might well ask if there are any Kates as in **The Taming of the Shrew** still abroad, willing to be so tamed?

At the time, ugliness and deformity were considered as God's judgment on an evil soul and so it would have seemed perfectly acceptable for the noble Prospero to treat Caliban with cruelty and disdain.

Prospero: *Thou most lying slave,*
Whom stripes may move, not kindness! I have us'd thee
(Filth as thou art) with human care, and lodg'd thee
In mine own cell, till thou didst, seek to violate
The honour of my child.

The Tempest   act 1 scene 2

Prospero's behaviour at this stage is typical of the unfeeling arrogance and greedy exploitation that was practised and encouraged by the rulers of most European states in the 16th and 17th centuries. Caliban is a savage and Christians were then thought to be at liberty to take the lands of savages and reduce their inhabitants to servitude. It also reflects very closely the manner of the early settlers of the New World, being friendly to the original inhabitants when in a position of weakness but changing rapidly with growing strength, first to cruel exploitation of the native population and then to the horrors of the slave trade.

However, Shakespeare moves well beyond the mores of the time and portrays Caliban in great depth as a savage in his exterior appearance and manners but as one who is redeemed by the spirit and imagination which lights him from within.

Think too of the developing attitude towards the Jew, Shylock. Anti-Semitism was rife and he was reviled as a harsh money-lender who unreasonably demands his dues. Indeed the phrase 'he insists on his pound of flesh' is still used in a derogatory way even today. Yet in spite of the generally unsympathetic treatment, Shakespeare still moves us to see him as a human being, most notably in a speech which would satisfy even the most politically correct in our own time.

Shylock: *Hath not a Jew eyes? hath not a Jew hands, organs, dimensions, senses, affections, passions? fed with the same food, hurt with the same weapons, subject to the same diseases, healed by the same means, warmed and cooled by the same winter and summer, as a Christian is? If you prick us, do we not bleed? if you tickle us, do we not laugh? if you poison us, do we not die? and if you wrong us, shall we not revenge? If we are like you in the rest, we will resemble you in that.*

The Merchant of Venice   act 3 scene 1

Shakespeare's farewell

Perhaps Shakespeare's last appearance as an actor on stage was in **The Tempest**. We certainly know that he retired from acting to concentrate on writing and business at about this time and it seems almost certain that Shakespeare wrote this play specifically for performance at Court. He undoubtedly introduced many elements that would appeal to the showy tastes of a court audience. New theatrical styles from Italy and France were all the rage, especially the processional dance sequences that formed an integral part of the Court Masques. King James adored watching the elegant movements and supple bodies of the young male dancers. "Will they not dance? Curse on them, why have I been brought here if they will not dance!' was the King's angry reaction to a performance in Oxford that had not provided for his tastes.

Shakespeare avoided that shaming experience by making Prospero devise entertainments for his guests which neatly supply the masque dance form without too seriously interrupting the story. Nowadays, the appearance of goddesses to dance and make flattering speeches, are considered rather boring and they are often cut. The somewhat sycophantic message that an anointed prince must not be put aside, even if he has long since failed in his duties, is not one to please an audience today. However, it would have most certainly appealed to King James. This theme is usually played down by modern directors, but the ideas of absolute rule and 'The Divine Right of Kings' were at the time very powerful. These ideas were also among the major causes of the Civil War and the execution of King Charles I, some thirty years later.

Shakespeare let it be known that he wished to retire into the country and be remembered as a 'gentleman poet', rather than as a man of the theatre.

Although this is not the last of his plays, I like to think that at the first Court performance Shakespeare himself played Prospero (he was noted for his playing of kingly roles) and that he spoke these closing lines directly to the King.

Now my charms are all o'erthrown,
And what strength I have's my own,
Which is most faint: now 'tis true,
I must be here confined by you,
Or sent to Naples. Let me not,
Since I have my dukedom got
And pardoned the deceiver, dwell
In this bare Island by your spell;
But release me from my bands
With the help of your good hands:
Gentle breath of yours my sails
Must fill, or else my project fails,
Which was to please. Now I want
Spirits to enforce, art to enchant,
And my ending is despair,
Unless I be relieved by prayer,
Which pierces so that it assaults
Mercy itself and frees all faults.
As you from crimes would pardon'd be,
Let your indulgence set me free.

The Tempest epilogue

Stage Effects

Music and sound effects formed an important part of a performance in Shakespeare's time and in **The Tempest** it was an essential ingredient. This was a time when great musical experiments were taking place and instructions for the sound effects were written into the dialogue. The musicians were sometimes divided into small groups and placed in different parts of the theatre, including under the stage. Echo effects were just one example of the possibilities this multi-phonic arrangement provided and for the first time, composers noted down when to play loudly and when to play softly. Drums and trumpets were sounded for 'Royal' entries and sometimes cannons were fired to add warlike effects. In fact it was one such royal salute, in 1613, that set fire to the thatched roof of the first Globe Theatre and caused it to burn to the ground. Thunder was produced by rolling one or more large stone balls across the floor of 'The Heavens' and all these effects were included or implied in the original stage directions.

Conjuring tricks were also used - for example in **The Tempest**, the banquet disappears at the instant of Ariel's command. This was most probably done with the help of a pivoting table top. On one side the feast would be set out and fixed in position on the reverse side the table would have one or two of Prospero's books, a pen etc. If the table had a cloth over it covering the legs it would obviously mask what was hidden underneath. In my experience, this is far more difficult to achieve on a stage like that of the Globe, with the audience sitting on three sides, than on a proscenium stage like the court theatre, where the audience had only a limited view. Such effects, when achieved, added considerably to the mystery and magic of the theatrical occasion.

Blood and gore of course had to be presented convincingly as the audience was already well used to seeing horrific acts of public torture and execution. Although it was possible for an actor to pierce a bladder of pig's blood hidden inside his costume, the almost impossible problem of cleaning his clothing for the next performance suggests that in this case the costumes would have to have been of the simplest kind. For duels, it would therfore have seemed reasonable for the contestants to strip off their doublets and fight in their shirts, so reducing the extent of the problem. Another approach, which was used on other occasions, demanded a second, already bloodied, costume to be made ready for the actor to change into. He could do this quickly off-stage and then re-enter, wounded, perhaps to make his dying speech.

Scenery

With the impressive examples of entertainment at the Court, first in Italy and then in France, it was not long before similar spectacles were mounted by the English Court. Amongst the most important developments was scenery that was capable of being quickly changed. It proved to be the most popular and influential innovation and would change the nature of performance and play writing for ever. Of course, elaborate scenery could become the most expensive part of a production and therefore was an ideal way to demonstrate the wealth and power of the sponsoring Prince. For the next two centuries, scenery was to become increasingly elaborate in execution and a demand was created for scenic artists skilled in such painting.

At first the revival of the ancient Greek scenic periaktoi was favoured. Rows of three or four three-sided columns, at either side of the stage, could be revolved to reveal a new face to the audience, each face decorated with a different scene.

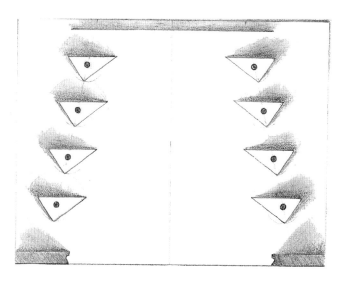

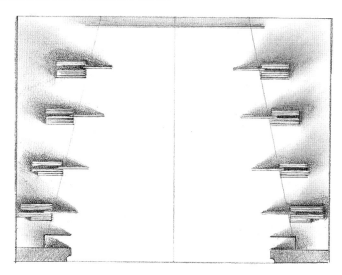

With Shakespeare's plays, three different scenes were insufficient to tell the story and new methods of scene changes were needed. A series of sliding screens or 'wings' proved to be the most satisfactory; they took up less space on the stage. By placing them in groups one behind the other, you could have as many scenes as the story dictated. Eventually the invention of a complicated linking system of ropes and pulleys allowed the screens be pulled on and off the stage simultaneously. Thus the audience could feel that they were transferred, for instance, from the sea-shore to Prospero's study and then to another part of the island, all in a matter of seconds, with no need to hold up the action, never a good idea in any production!

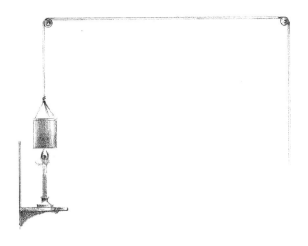

Some lighting effects were attempted on stage, although the auditorium remained fully lit at all times. The candles lighting the scenery could be dimmed by metal drum like shades which could be dropped over the flames by cords suspended on pulleys, coloured glass shades could add effect for certain scenes. All this however probably caused just one more fire hazard as the cords presumably could be set alight by the flame - chains would be too noisy - darkness falls silently, it doesn't clatter down!

Restoration theatre

The return of King Charles II to England in 1660 and his restoration to the throne, had a dramatic effect on the state of English theatrical life. During the Commonwealth, Puritan bigotry had succeeded in closing all public playhouses and theatres, throwing the actors and technicians out of work. Private performances had been allowed to continue in wealthy households but the great days of Shakespeare's popular theatre had gone, seemingly for ever. Even the Globe Theatre, rebuilt after the fire of 1613, had been pulled down, as the landowners found it more profitable to use the site for housing and commercial properties. Royal patronage re-emerged within a few months of the King's arrival. Two new theatres were built in London to cater for the small privileged group of courtiers and officials who had seen entertainments during their exile on the Continent. Many new developments in theatrical architecture and techniques had been developed in France during the interregnum and they were now to burst into bloom in England. Other theatres opened although they were not granted a royal patent (licence) to perform plays and would have been heavily fined if they did. Their managers therefore introduced song and dance routines interspersed with scenes from the great plays and short sketches by new writers. Thomas Killigrew, under the King's licence, was one of the two managers allowed to present complete plays and Shakespeare was again performed in public. The reception was disappointing. Fashions had changed and the audiences found Shakespeare's language and word play tedious and incomprehensible. The elegant courtiers wanted plays that reflected their own lifestyle. Authors like Farquhar, Congreve and Vanbrugh obliged with plays written in imitation of French fashions, all froth and innuendo, laced with a great deal of snobbery. Audiences may have found Shakespeare difficult to follow but actors could not resist the glorious opportunities he provided for the demonstration of their art. Huge amendments to the original texts were made in an attempt to regain popularity and box office success.

Perhaps the most important change to arrive from France was the introduction of professional actresses. For the first time great female roles such as Lady Macbeth, Juliet, Cleopatra, Portia, Ophelia and Gertrude were portrayed by women, not boys and young men. The results were sensational but also introduced a few problems. So often Shakespeare's women dress up successfully as young men and remain miraculously unrecognised by their friends and lovers. Now real women dressed as men, in knee breeches, drew the crowds of sensation-seeking gallants. At that time, women's legs were never exposed in public. In addition, it was rather more difficult to be convinced by the ludicrous situations, where their lovers fail to recognise these curious chested boys for what they are.

Rosalind: *I charge you, O men, for the love you bear to women,*
as I perceive by your simpering, none of you hates them,
that between you and the women the play may please.
If I were a woman ...

As You Like It epilogue

Surely this last sentence must have raised an unintended laugh.

Restoration theatres were built in the form that we now normally think of when talking about the stage. A proscenium arch separated the stage from the auditorium with a space directly in front of the stage for the musicians. The 'pit', nowadays called 'the stalls' was surrounded on the three remaining sides by galleries, divided into boxes. These boxes were often hired for the season by wealthy customers. The third tier was left undivided to be used by people unable to afford the more expensive positions. Unfortunately the old Elizabethan habit of members of the public sitting at the side of the stage, to show off and make interruptions during the performance continued.

The scenery was still the old established style with sliding wings, back cloths, flying cloths and borders but the new theatres were built with a 'flying tower' and 'grid', which allowed large pieces to 'fly' upwards completely out of the audience's view. All these mechanisms remain in use today.

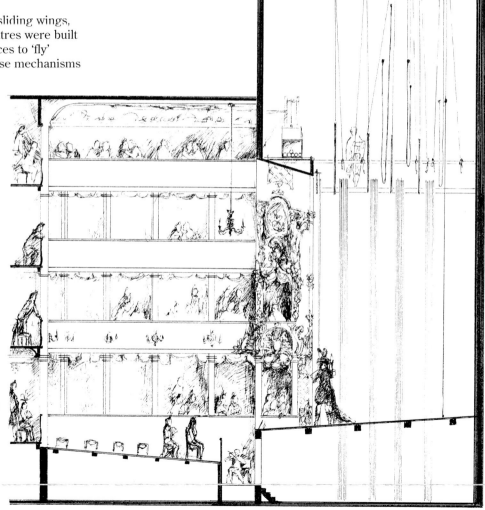

Actors and actresses were unhappy to be seen in anything but the latest fashions. 'Roman' costumes might be worn for the heroic Roman plays by men but they refused to appear without their periwigs. Cleopatra would be seen in a variation of court dress, with a head-dress resembling the fashionable fontange. Every 'classical' tragedian's head would be adorned with great nodding plumes of ostrich feathers, called a 'panache'. Even today, the expression 'performed with panache' is used to describe a production of particular style and energy. Think of nodding ostrich plumes when you next hear it!

Some attempts at historical accuracy were made for the history plays but only for the leading roles. There were some bizarre effects when, for example, Henry the Eighth, dressed like the Holbein portraits, but minus the codpiece, appeared surrounded by his courtiers in the newly fashionable 'Persian coats', lace cravats, high heels and huge wigs.

Wigs & periwigs

Every age has its idea of realism and Hamlet's instruction to the players is always referred to, by actors, with a sort of reverence. The formalised gestures, expressions and method of speaking, established in the late 17th century would not, I suspect, have pleased Shakespeare and would probably leave us falling on the floor with laughter. In spite of Hamlet's dislike of 'Periwig-pated fellows', the Hamlets of the late 17th century would not be seen without one. In fact, the audience of the time would not be able to accept the possibility of a royal prince appearing at court without the luxuriant curls that were worn every-where by men of means and position. As in Shakespeare's time, Hamlet, like all courtiers, would normally wear a hat in public both indoors and out. The observance of a highly complicated, and carefully graded, set of rules governing the precise degree of raising your hat or removing it altogether, according to the social position of the person you greeted, continued to be of prime importance for any man wishing to succeed in society.

Hamlet: *Put your bonnet to his right use; tis for the head.*
Osric: *I thank your lordship, it is very hot.*
Hamlet: *No, believe me, tis very cold; the wind is northerly.*
Osric: *It is indifferent cold, my lord, indeed.*
Hamlet: *But yet methinks it is very sultry and hot, or my complexion.*
Osric: *Exceedingly, my lord; it is very sultry, as 'twere,*
        I cannot tell how. But, my lord his majesty bade me
        signify to you that he has laid a great wager on your head: sir,
        this is the matter,-
Hamlet: *I beseech you, remember,-*
(Hamlet moves him to put on his hat but Osric still declines to do so)

Hamlet   act 5 scene 2

Everyone at the time would have enjoyed this moment in the play, in fact there would have been new possibilities for humour, apart from the old ridiculing of an over obsequious courtier unable to relax in the presence of royalty. There were now many fashion conscious men who merely used their hats as a lavish decoration to be carried rather than worn. Their enormous and elaborate wigs were easily damaged by the constant removal and replacement of their hats. Osric would almost certainly have been portrayed as a fop desperately concerned with his periwig, in an agony of indecision not wishing to disoblige his prince but at the same time terrified that his blond curls would be disarranged if he did as Hamlet told him to do.

Henry Townsend's Journal, September 1698

Now I must record my triumphant debut as a 'Man of the Theatre'. It is seldom that a painter receives such praise, such noisy acclamation at each rising of the curtain. Shakespeare's genius is quite eclipsed! All talk of the excellence of the scenery, the perfect representation of Elsinore, the exquisite details of the Queen's Closet and the magnificence of the Throne Room. The Countess has admired my talents for four years, perhaps more, so it was no surprise that I should assume responsibility for the mise en scene for her latest toy - her private theatre. Last night, my place at table, on my charmer's right hand, remained empty, much to her chagrin, but I determined to complete the cloth for the grave digger's scene. I painted in mounting anger, overlooked by the grinning skull of some poor wretch animated by the meagre flicker of my only candle. Overcome by rage and to the astonishment of all, I stormed through the enfilade and snatched a candelabrum from the table. I returned to my labours and would have worked through the night had not, at two of the morning, my own sweet charmer come with a summons I could not refuse for politeness nor indeed my own passion's sake! The labours of the night ended with the greatest satisfaction, though not completed as I had intended!

The cut-out pieces for this scene are on page 45. The instructions on how to assemble it are on page 44.

This area glues to page 19

This page becomes the base of a three-dimensional pop-up scene telling the story of a performance in 1698 of Hamlet at the private theatre of Countess Devorny. It is told by Henry Townsend, artist and protégé of the Countess. To create it:

1. Remove page 17 completely from the book by cutting along the solid line.
2. Cut out the T-shaped piece precisely by cutting around the solid outline.
3. Score along the dotted line and fold it towards you to make a valley fold. Crease firmly to make a hinged flap.

4. Check that the top of the T fits over this grey shaded area and that the hinged flap covers the text beneath. Then glue this flap carefully into position. It then forms the backdrop for the theatre scene.
5. The remaining pieces to complete this scene are on page 45 and the detailed instructions are given on page 44.

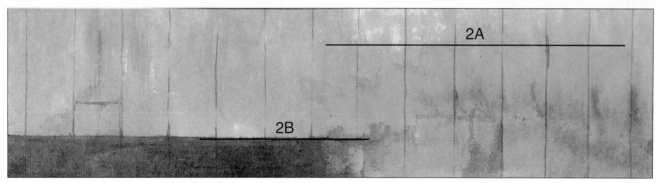

The Countess and her friends are much to be thanked for such generosity and spirited support for this enterprise but for myself, I must own, that the play, in performance, moved me but little; Such convolutions and obscurity of language completely addle the brain and loose all understanding. Mr Cibber's execution of the role of Osric was a gem amongst dross, providing the only laughs of the evening on stage. Always excepting, our own witty observations on the aged corpulent Hamlet and his mother, young enough to be his daughter! Mrs B, she may be, but actress she is not!

I must own that when the Ghost appeared to walk through the walls of Gertrude's closet, even I, who had painted the wings, was taken by surprise. Mr B's famous interpretation of Hamlet's horror at the sight of his father's ghost has however become too much of a ritual. His stepping back in fear and knocking over the chair seems all too contrived, but the resulting crash served only to wake the Countess's father who had been interjecting loud snores throughout the scene, completely drowning out the screams and groans of Polonius behind the arras, much to the amusement of all.

The grave digger's scene moved us all to silence and awe. My final cloth of the churchyard seemed to have rekindled a spark of inspiration to Mr B's performance of 'Alas, poor Yorick!'

The actors were incapable of hiding their displeasure as I took my bows. Mr & Mrs B in particular were much put out, as every time they walked forward and acknowledged the applause, the audience called me back to be greeted with ever greater huzzars. I have noticed before that there is a sad unwillingness on the part of actors to recognise talent in others!

Bringing light to the stage

The theatres built in the 18th century improved and enlarged the stage and its machinery. The wings, arranged in groups and painted with astonishingly convincing perspective were helped in their effect by the raking of the stage floor. The back of the stage was higher than the front. In some of the smaller theatres, the rake was so steep that it gave the actors some problems. Either they were struggling up hill, or they found themselves almost unable to stop, when going towards the audience. The expressions 'upstage' 'downstage' still remain in stage directions even though few modern theatres have raked stages.

Lighting was still achieved by complicated arrangements of candles. At the back of each set of wings, there was a stack of candle holders that operated on a pulley to light the next set of wings. As each candle was lit, the pulley would lift it off the stack and a second candle could be placed in position. It in turn would be lifted to allow a third candle to be lit and so on, until the whole height of the wings was evenly lit. The brilliance of the scenic artist did the rest. Candles need a great deal of attention. It took a long time to light the hundreds of candles needed to illuminate the stage sufficiently. If the proportion of wax in relation to the wick is even slightly wrong then the candle either goes out or it 'gutters'. This means that the wax melts too quickly and pours down the side of the candle causing the flame to enlarge dangerously and to smoke heavily. Even when they are burning perfectly, candles need to be trimmed from time to time and an attendant was employed to do this during the performance.

Imagine how unnerving it must have been for an actor in the midst of his great speech when a man, carrying candle trimmers on a long stick, walked on stage and proceeded to trim candles and then, if he did this with sufficient aplomb, received a round of applause from the audience!

Fire was a constant hazard especially for actresses in the voluminous panniered costumes that formed an essential requirement for most roles. Queens of tragedy and comedy alike, suffered terrible injuries and even died as a result of their costumes catching fire from one of the naked flames in the footlights or the wings.

A disrespectful public

In the 18th century, acting was not considered to be a respectable profession and actors and actresses were rather looked down upon by the middle class folk who were the major part of the theatre-going public. Performers had to put up with abuse and disrespect from their audiences, some of whom were sitting in boxes built on the side of the stage itself. Why anyone would want to sit on the side of the stage, where none of the painted scenery with its clever perspective could be seen, might be thought baffling. However, the stage is undoubtedly the best place to be seen by the rest of the audience and many bright wits needed publicity for themselves. So, dressed in the latest fashions and loudly making smart comments at the expense of the performers, they were able to achieve the notoriety that they sought.

Towards the end of the century, there were two great performers and they were able to put a stop to all this nonsense. David Garrick and Sarah Siddons both gained acceptance into high society by their great talent and by their respectable, ordered, private lives. In the case of Mrs. Siddons this was doubly astonishing, as she was saddled with a drunken husband who claimed to be her manager and drank his way through almost every penny she earned on stage.

David Garrick was luckier. With his wife he was able to build a splendid house near the palace at Hampton Court. Mrs Garrick was an Austrian ballet dancer and was often visited at home by Queen Charlotte, the wife of George III. On at least one occasion they peeled potatoes and did ordinary household chores together. This must have been a welcome escape into a more ordinary life for poor Queen Charlotte as she struggled to bear the heartbreak of watching her husband decline into madness.

With his position in society so well established, Garrick refused to continue his performances until the audience was quiet! Having an astonishing talent for public relations, he recreated the Shakespeare legend, although never fearing to alter and rewrite large sections of the plays! He also set in motion the popularity of Stratford-upon-Avon as a tourist attraction.

Shakespeare was performed in complete versions at the two rival patent Theatres in London. David Garrick at Drury Lane and the Kembles at Covent Garden but Shakespearean scenes were sometimes performed in other theatres as well, mixed in a potpourri of songs and dances to overcome the old ban on unpatented performance of straight plays. In fact, most people enjoyed these additions.

This was an age of reaction against the rigid symmetry of the Baroque style, which was now replaced by scenery that allowed for more realistic and dramatic representations of wild heaths and castle battlements.

Costumes too began to achieve some sense of place and history. Although actors still appeared in fashionable clothes, they would on occasion add historical touches to suggest a mediaeval character or an Egyptian queen. However, the Elizabethan ruff was so fixed in peoples minds as being of the age of Shakespeare that, well into the 19th century, it was almost an essential piece of costume for both actors and actresses, whether they were playing Richard III, Hamlet, Lady Macbeth or Titania.

But omne bene, say I, being of an old father's mind,
Many can brook the weather, that love not the wind.

Love's Labour's Lost act 4 scene 2

Mrs Siddons' style of speech, together with that of her brother John Philip Kemble, was frequently referred to as 'The Kemble Style' and dominated the English stage for thirty years. The style was static and classical in contrast to the 'realism' of Garrick or the 'romantic passion' of Edmund Kean.

Although Mrs. Siddons was best in tragic roles, she must have had a sense of humour, for when a little girl asked her why she always pronounced wind as 'winde' she replied, drawing herself up to look down her famously long nose, 'I can finde it in my minde to call it winde but I cannot find it in my mind to call it wind!'

Audiences in the early 18th century wanted to be entertained and disapproved of unhappy endings. They were not particularly interested in Shakespeare's beautiful language and poetry and large chunks were cut away or rewritten for the occasion. Richard III and Shylock were the popular villains that the audience loved to hate but it was the comedies, especially the unaristocratic **The Merry Wives of Windsor**, that satisfied the rather sentimental morality of the merchant class families that now filled the boxes on most occasions.

By the beginning of the 19th century it was novelty and variety that drew the crowds. They came to witness bleeding chunks of the 'best' of Shakespeare, short scenes or soliloquies, which were performed out of context in a mixed entertainment. Often, performances were given by child actors, their tiny diminutive forms and squeaky voices pronouncing the finest lines of Shakespeare, such as 'Once more into the breech dear friends ...', 'Out, out, damned spot ...', 'What light from yonder window breaks? ...' and so on. Such unimaginable horrors thrilled audiences who flocked to see the latest child wonder and paid handsomely to do so.

A typical example of these hotch-potch entertainments was advertised in this way:

> **The celebrated little actor Master Carey,**
> not yet eleven years old,
> is to present a benefit evening for his mother.
> ### In the great room of No 8 Store Street, Bedford Square.
> on Tuesday 17th March 1801.
>
> *In an inimitable exhibition*
> as it has been played before an assembly of Ladies of the Aristocracy
> and of the best society, with unusual approval.
> **A talent, rare in one so young,**
> **unmatched and rarely seen before now.**
> Part I.
> An introductory lecture followed by *Pizarro and Blue Beard*,
> Part II.
> *Richard III* and *Naval Pillar* (where Hamlet writes and inserts a letter.)
> A song executed by a lady.
> Part III.
> *Speed the Plough* and *Feudal Times*.
>
> **Entrance one Shilling.**

Perhaps the evening was more enjoyable than it sounds. Master Carey, whose real name was Edmund Kean, became one of the greatest actors of his time and his revolutionary style completely eclipsed the Kembles' static style of acting and recitation. His body was never still, his eyes rarely closed, all was animation, and his voice! Never had the theatre contained such passion.

Lord Byron, when he had seen Kean play **Richard III**, wrote:

By Jove! Here is a soul,
life, nature, truth
without exaggeration or diminution ....
Richard is a man, and Kean is Richard.

Lord Byron was probably more accurate than he realised.

After a performance of **Richard III**, Kean was found by his son in the street outside the theatre, sword in hand, menacing people as they hurried by, shouting 'Dickon, thy master is bought and sold!' and 'I think there be six Richmonds in the field, five have I slain today instead of him' and 'A horse! a horseπ! my kingdom for a horse!' Kean was indeed Richard and had to be restrained and taken home.

Kean continued working and entertaining theatre audiences until he finally slipped into insanity and died at his home in Richmond, Surrey, on 15th May 1833.

The Victorian theatre

The reign of Queen Victoria was to become the longest in British history and it defined an era. In the theatre, the Victorian era was a time of great change. When Victoria came to the throne in 1837 gas lighting was just being introduced into the theatre and this revolutionised the production style for all branches of the performing arts. Shakespeare was once more squeezed into a new mould.

The most dramatic change, of course, was that the auditorium lights could be dimmed while the lights on stage remained bright. We playgoers are rather like parrots who are silenced by placing a cloth over their cages. At last the audience could be pushed into the completely passive roll that Garrick had fought so hard to achieve. Removed from contact with the actors, first by the proscenium arch and then by the ever present footlights and the orchestra pit, the audience could no longer do more than watch and listen. There were noisy elements still, but with the auditorium now darkened, the individual felt cut off from all but a few of his companions. The games and fun that could be had from looking at other members of the audience was now only possible at the beginning and the end of a performance or during an interval.

At last the actors had the attention of all, or had they? Gaslight could be very much brighter than candles, flat painted scenery tended to be bleached out - flattened by its brilliance. Solidly built realistic scenery began to replace the easily moved and cheap to build flats for most productions. Shakespeare had to compete with the newest 'realistic' plays by authors like Robertson, who provided domestic drama in settings with real doors, ceilings and quantities of real furniture.

Victorian audiences began to care more and more for historical accuracy and demanded spectacular realism, if they were to be persuaded to sit through what many of them thought of as high falutin', difficult language. Variable lighting could produce sensational effects but the more that reality was demanded, the slower the performances became. Intervals were introduced in order that the cumbersome scenery could be changed, without the audience becoming impatient. However, these breaks in concentration meant that the actors had to re-engage their audience's attention at the beginning of each and every scene.

When Beerbohm-Tree staged **A Midsummer Night's Dream** at Her Majesty's Theatre, in London, the audience was enchanted by the live rabbits that ran amongst the realistic trees and undergrowth while fairies flew and disappeared with the help of wires, lighting and gauzes. It seemed that the ultimate spectacle had been achieved. Not so! Other theatres were equipped to stage horse races on moving belts and poor Shakespeare was hard put to it to keep his audiences. A production of **Henry V** had the King and several of his train riding into Harfleur mounted on real chargers!

Such lavish expenditure, of course, had to be paid for and it was no longer possible to change plays in repertory. In order to recover their costs, managers hoped that their productions would run for a long time and planned their season with this in mind. This in turn led to the reorganisation of the auditorium. It was no longer worth paying for a box for the whole season if plays were not to be changed frequently and so the walls dividing the boxes were, for the most part, removed to form what we now call 'The Dress Circle' and 'The Circle'.

Ellen Bowman's Journal, September 1888

Tonight I am taking Fred and Alice and also Jack and Ethel and their children to see 'Romeo and Juliet'. It is to be my treat, after all it is the last time we can all be together for goodness knows how long. Alice and Fred are returning to Berlin tomorrow and I sail for Calcutta at the end of the month to stay with Albert and Sujeet for the winter. I have reserved seats in the 'dress circle' which I am assured have a good view, though not in the centre. I shall take my opera glasses with me in any case. Alice is pleased to be seeing 'Romeo and Juliet' once more because, she says, it reminds her of 'Dear Papa' who loved it so. It was indeed one of Hypolite's favourite plays and so has become dear to me. I shall wear my new mauve silk gown from Liberty's. It will be most suitable for this special evening.

This afternoon I told the children the story of the Montagues and Capulets and tried to get them to learn those wonderful speeches: 'O Romeo, Romeo! wherefore art thou, Romeo?' and 'Tis almost morning; I would have thee gone', using the dining table as the balcony. However, after a while, Romeo became bored and splashed lemonade on Juliet's dress! Shakespeare did not write the ensuing scene with nurse! However, after this evening, I'm sure that they will want to learn the whole play by heart, every word!

The cut-out pieces for this scene are on page 47. The instructions on how to assemble it are on page 44.

This page becomes the base of a three-dimensional pop-up scene telling the story of a visit to Her Majesty's Theatre in 1888 by Ellen Bowman, her children, their spouses and her two grandchildren. To create it:

1. Remove page 27 completely from the book by cutting along the solid line.
2. Cut out the T-shaped piece precisely by cutting around the solid outline.
3. Score along the dotted line and fold it towards you to make a valley fold. Crease firmly to make a hinged flap.

4. Check that the top of the T fits over this grey shaded area and that the hinged flap covers the text beneath. Then glue this flap carefully into position. It then forms the backdrop for the theatre scene.
5. The remaining pieces to complete this scene are on page 45 and the detailed instructions are given on page 44.

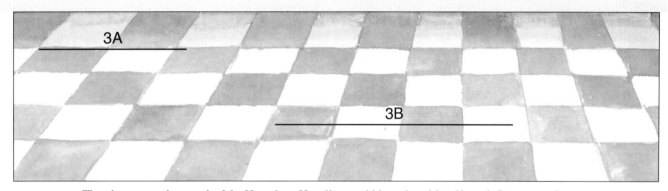

3A

3B

The play was quite wonderful. How dear Hypolite would have loved it. Ah me! It seems so long ago when we were newly wed and first wept together at the death of the star-crossed lovers. But enough of this sadness, I have wept enough for a month! Such brilliant acting and the wonderful Renaissance costumes were a treat to be savoured. Fred and Alice, though, were slightly critical of the balcony scene saying it was supposed to be in an orchard, yet there was not a fruit tree in sight and that the fountain was too noisy. I thought it was redolent of love's passion.

We became so involved in this discussion that we were still talking when the curtain went up on the next scene. It was only when a man's voice from the back said 'Lets 'ave a bit of hush, Madam!' that we realised what we were doing. How embarrassing! The whole audience seemed convulsed with suppressed mirth. I must have turned bright red but fortunately the house lights dimmed and everyone began to admire the lighting effects on stage. It so perfectly captured the feeling of the day dawning in Italy.

The interval seemed interminable and the crush allowed no possibility of sitting down. I was shocked to see that when the children said they were bored, Ethel decided she would take them home, instead of insisting that they should wait until the end of the play. It was very weak of her and rather spoilt this special evening. Jack was sent out to hail a cab and, miracle of miracles, found one. Ethel bundled the children into the Hansom and pulled the doors and windows shut. In the rush, the cab drove off with the train of her evening gown hanging out from under the door! Poor Jack was in a terrible state of irritation, but we managed to persuade him to stay with us until the end.

New ideas for a new century

The beginning of the new century and then the death of Queen Victoria in 1901 was thought to mark the end of an era, and so it did. In the theatre at the turn of the century the presentation of Shakespeare's plays had become locked and stultified into the pedantic 'reality' of the previous decades. With the cumbersome over-built sets, uninspired lighting and a slowness in the delivery of speech that, when we hear it - for the invention of the gramophone at this time allows us to hear Sir Henry Irving and other performers intone the words of Shakespeare - makes it impossible for us to understand how an audience could bear to sit through a whole performance; atmospherics and historical accuracy or no! The established 'serious' theatre managements, headed by Irving at the Lyceum Theatre in London believed that their style was definitive; nothing could be more real and no other companies could match their lavish, spectacular productions. Most of their audience would have agreed and would have loved the barbaric splendours of a scene like this for the opening of **King Lear**. Costumes were every bit as lavish and 'historically correct' as the scenery they were seen against, with every detail seemingly fighting for supremacy, and the actors were dwarfed and barely visible above the heraldic motifs of their medieval tabards.

Artistic integrity had finally died, or so it seemed to many artistic souls, but a new wave of revolutionary experiments was about to breath fresh life into the playing of Shakespeare.

A few young people dreamt of a new theatre, with all but the bare necessities swept away.

Simplicity and light

It was the brilliantly versatile son of the famous actress, Ellen Terry, who was most influential in promoting the new style. Edward Gordon Craig was an actor, director, designer, writer and illustrator and through his writings and exhibitions of his designs, passionately argued that drama should rid the stage of all the fussy pedantry that cluttered performances and slowed the action almost to a halt.

Craig's visual ideas were not entirely original. He always acknowledged his debt to Adolph Appia, the Swiss musician and theatre reformer who had so criticised the staging of Wagner's operas in the 1890's. Appia had complained of the lack of unity between the music and the stage presentation and demanded the abandonment of solid realistic scenery. He campaigned for sets to be based on straight lines where the acting levels were linked by staircases or ramps. He insisted that only the human form should provide the movement and the curves to complete the visual composition. Throughout his lifetime Appia remained principally a musician and it was only after his death that his stage drawings were published.

In the meantime, Craig had designed and produced in 1911, at the Moscow Arts Theatre, one of the most influential Shakespearean productions ever. His new version of **Hamlet** was a revelation, with simple vertical screens which formed seemingly endless variations of settings and scenes. There was the horizontal emphasis of large flights of steps to provide superb acting areas at different levels and, when lit with coloured lighting, beautifully conveyed the darkness of night and the brilliance of the Court. Everything was perfectly expressed within the same area. There was no need for painted scenery, no need for anything but furniture of the simplest form. What an astonishing change!

Everything that Appia had demanded was there and it worked. In fact there were one or two teething problems, but in spite of this, the production was to change the course of set design for the next 40 to 50 years.

So much of this revolution was made possible by the introduction of electricity into the theatre. Like all new inventions the earliest attempts at the end of the nineteenth century were cumbersome and inefficient but the advantages even these primitive lamps offered soon convinced theatre managements of their value. More brilliant than gas light and a great deal safer to use, electricity had another great advantage. It was so much easier to move, adjust and group lamps attached to electric cables than gas tubing. Focusing and filtering the lamps had, of course, been possible in the eighteenth century but the dramatic and rapid improvement in the design and effectiveness of electric lamps, the supply of electricity and the dimming racks that controlled the amount

of light each individual lamp produced, made it possible, for the first time in history, to completely change a scene and concentrate the audience's attention by light alone.

Fortuny's Cupola

The Wagner family embraced these new ideas completely for their opera productions at Bayreuth but in England it took longer to convince the theatrical establishment of the magical effects that could be achieved so simply. The rapid improvements in lighting technology and the comparative cheapness of the scenery was probably the strongest reason for these new ideas to be accepted.

Another young man, this time a Spaniard living in Italy, was to provide a further brilliant idea to simplify scenic design. It was one that gave an astonishing feeling of limitless space. Mariano Fortuny, now more famous for his exquisite pleated silk evening gowns, became interested in lighting technology and was irritated by the number of flats and borders necessary to mask out the ugly walls of the stage and to hide the actors waiting to make their entrances. He invented the 'Cupola Fortuny' which developed the advantage of the curved panorama by curving it upwards and forwards, forming the effect of half a dome. By doing this, nearly all the 'masking' could be eliminated.

In fact no scenery at all was needed, an actor could stand, apparently on a flat open landscape with nothing but him and the horizon. A folding version of this dome idea was tried out in Paris as early as 1902 but proved too cumbersome. He then devised an inflatable version for a performance in Berlin. German theatre managements took this experimental development very seriously and a permanent cupola of concrete was built at the Deutsches Theatre in Berlin during the 1920's.

Simplicity through necessity!

The extreme simplicity that was so much admired in Germany and Russia, between the wars, was never entirely embraced in England. A kind of purity and functionalism influenced productions but few went without some form of decoration to set a place or historical period. The effects of the drastic limitations imposed on the Theatre and indeed everyone, by the government during the 1940's had the most astonishing result. Instead of promoting the ideas of simplicity of design, there was a revival of the old historicism. But whereas in the Victorian Theatre lavish expenditure had been the rule now, with the imposition of rationing on all materials necessary for a production, it became necessary to look for simple and inexpensive ways to achieve results. Simplicity was imposed by necessity. Directors and audiences expected their productions to look spectacular and it was the responsibility of the designers to come up with lavish seeming results, using the minimal amounts of cloth and construction materials. A room in a palace could be represented by a single vertical piece, built with simplified three dimensional reality that wouldn't be flattened by the bright lights. A flight of stairs made from stock rostra that could be re-arranged and re-used for every play, season after season would be all that was necessary to convince the audiences that they were looking at an exotic scene. Costumes and props that looked convincingly rich and historical were made up from old curtains and bits of 'tat' from the local flea markets and even from items found on bomb sites. Over painting and felt shapes appliquéd on to re-dyed fabrics were found to produce wonderful effects and it was amazing what fine jewellery could be made from old lavatory chains, felt and buttons!

The cinema, a new romanticism

Thanks to the passionate insistence of the intellectuals striving for perfection and simplicity, Shakespeare in the theatre had become increasingly removed from a popular audience. All the theorising and stripping away of everything superfluous from the play was thrilling and satisfying for only a small intellectual elite and to a large extent, this limited the audiences to the middle class. Performances were approached in the most reverential manner by audiences dressed in all their evening finery.

They delighted in showing their superior knowledge of 'The Bard' while discussing the finer points of meaning in the scenes they had just witnessed, over their interval drinks. The glitter of their conversation was nowhere near the sparkle of sequined gowns and diamond studs of their dress but the sense of social superiority they experienced was intoxicating.

Most people, even if they could afford the tickets for the theatre felt unable to spend money on the obligatory evening dress. A few students of literature or theatre enthusiasts were prepared to pay the small amount for a hard bench seat in 'The Gods' but for most people the discomfort and humiliation of climbing the concrete back stairs to watch 'starkly beautiful' exquisitely spoken poetry, was not worth the trouble. Especially as just round the corner, for the same price, you could feel welcome in your ordinary clothes, at a cinema where all sorts of astonishing, glamourous spectacles and hilarious comedies would lift you away into another world.

In 1927 the 'Movies' became the 'Talkies'. The technology of synchronised, recorded sound had developed sufficiently to allow Al Jolson to sing and talk in 'The Jazz Singer' and created a sensation. Stage actors, with their trained voices, then found themselves being offered wealth and fame on a scale they had never dreamt of. Only two years later, Shakespeare moved into Hollywood, with the help of some additional words by the film director, Samuel Taylor and **The Taming of the Shrew** starring Mary Pickford and Douglas Fairbanks. The two designers, William Cameron Menzies and Laurence Irving, ignored all the functionalist dogmas of the past few decades and produced joyous, realistic, solidly built and lavishly decorated sets of a quality that Beerbohm-Tree could only have dreamt of.

Of course with film there was no need to move scenery you simply moved the camera. The argument for simplicity collapsed.

Shakespeare as propaganda had been used by Queen Elizabeth's favourite, the Earl of Essex when **Richard II** was performed as a prelude to his rebellion of 1601.

In the desperate years of the 1940's, a brilliant young actor, Laurence Olivier, was released from his military service and provided money and support by the British government, to produce, direct and play the leading roll in a film version of **Henry V**. It was intended to be a war time morale booster for the Nation, but Olivier did more than provide a boost to Britain's battered morale, he created a masterpiece. In fact the film was not released until after the War in 1946. Somehow, he had managed to produce a film that appealed to a huge popular audience, whilst at the same time employing a design team that created an astonishingly stylised visual effect, based on the medieval illustrations in 'Très Riches Heures du Duc de Berry'.

This was taking theatrical style into the cinema with brilliant success. The sound track contained a wonderful orchestral score by William Walton that used the 15th Century 'Song of Agincourt' as a major theme. There was historical accuracy but not reality and the audiences loved it.

The huge immensity of the 'close up' has astonishing power to engage an audience's attention in a way that no theatre performance can hope to reproduce. Such images are accepted as realistic in spite of the grotesque magnification.

Two new inventions provided Shakespeare with new audiences. First was the 'Wireless'. Radio made it possible for thousands of people to hear the words of Shakespeare's plays even though they had never been to a theatre in their lives. In Britain the inauguration of the British Broadcasting Corporation under the guidance of Lord Reith, who had all the instincts of a severe but benign headmaster, made sure that countless productions of 'The Bard' were listened to by an enormous audience. Individuals and small family groups gathered round their wireless and were transported to 'The vasty fields of France', to Verona, Sicily, Rome or even Windsor Great Park. Radio was, and is, perfect for Shakespeare. All our concentration is focused on his words and, as he expected, we are free to conjure for ourselves what everyone and every place looks like.

By the mid 1950's, Television had arrived. In Britain, the BBC had a complete monopoly and only one channel, so the steadily growing audiences at home sat and watched whatever programmes appeared on their screens. The charter required that 'cultural' programmes should form a percentage of the programmes and Shakespeare was an absolute must. For the first time, productions of the plays could be seen as well as heard by the greater part of the population. Although many young viewers attending the new grammar schools, might have preferred 'The Quatermass Experiment', their examination studies required a knowledge of Shakespeare's texts. Watching television was the most enjoyable way to approach them and so the performance of Shakespeare underwent a considerable revival.

Of course all the sets were black and white and the television cameras were cumbersome and demanded a great deal of light. Even in the darkest scenes, powerful lamps were necessary. Also designers had problems because different colours often produced the most unexpected results when reduced to tones of dark grey, mid grey, pale grey and white on screen. Blues and reds were particularly unpredictable. In order to overcome this problem it was decided that all the scenery should be painted in standard tones of black, greys and white. This looked very well on screen and for a while these dismal monochrome sets were used for all productions. Unfortunately, the scenery had a depressing effect on the actors and made even the most brilliant performers act in a dull and turgid way.

Full colour sets were reintroduced and in any case the technology was improving rapidly. However, if a performer did not fit the costume supplied and had to be 'let out', then gussets of an 'appropriate tone' were inserted. These were not necessarily the right colour or fabric, but appeared on screen to be correct. However, for the actors in the studio it was easy to lose concentration when faced with such a bizarre mixture of stripes and patches!

The programmes went out live, so any mistakes or accidents were seen by millions of viewers. Sometimes they were not seen at all, as one unfortunate young actress was to discover. Having rehearsed her one and only entrance for three weeks, she found her way was blocked when the moment came. The cameras had moved to where she was supposed to be and the show went on without her! The presentation style for most television drama was realistic and everything was assembled in the studio on the day of transmission. For outdoor scenes large quantities of live tree branches were cut and brought into the television studio in the early hours of the morning so that camera rehearsals could start at ten. By the time the programme was transmitted in the evening, the leaves had drooped and withered under the heat of the lights and the whole studio stank of rotting vegetation!

Everything has changed since then. Colour television and rival production companies have produced the astonishing technical improvements of cameras, lighting, sound equipment and telerecording (which we now call video recording). The large television studios

are now rarely needed for drama productions. Everything is done on location and the audience no longer sees the accidents and mistakes that inevitably happen. All is edited and perfected in advance and you would think that the performance of Shakespeare live on stage would be doomed. However, although you cannot zoom in to a close up, or cross-fade and inter-cut the scenes, the theatre still has a special magic that draws the crowds. Shakespeare continues to enthral an audience and the theatre has gained new life as it has absorbed and adapted the techniques of film, television and computer technology to its own needs.

The theatre fights back

The need for the theatre to find new expression and forms of performance was never more insistent than in the 1960's. The reality of television and the massive splendour of film created a mood for change. Actors directors and designers searched for a different kind of reality, the reality of direct and powerful communication between actor and audience. Everything was to return to simplicity, but not the austere perfection of Appia or Craig. That relied too much on the passive reception of the audience and its admiration of pure style. Now, nothing must come between the audience and the characters and situations of the play.

Actors and directors looked for new performance spaces that could provide greater contact with an audience. They experimented with 'theatre in the round', where the audience sat on all sides of the stage, thrust stages, where the audience sat on three sides of the stage and flexible theatres where the stage could easily be changed from one form to another. Theatre complexes, like the National Theatre, with several stages linked by a central foyer were designed to accommodate all styles of performance.

Some of the most influential performances at this time came from the Royal Shakespeare Company and the National Theatre. The mood, on the whole, was simple and dark. The new lighting technology could provide astonishing effects on dark textured structures that could change and swing into different positions, thus providing new spaces for the action or to isolate a performer to give almost a cinematic concentration. By such techniques, the audience could be forced to look at only a small part of the stage.

For many, actors and critics alike, anything decorative was treated with the greatest suspicion. It might be allowed for a comedy but the search was for a 'concept', a 'visual metaphor', in which a performance could take place. Sometimes Shakespeare's genius was drowned by these ideas but more often, as in the case of the production of **A Midsummer Night's Dream**, by Peter Brook, the directors arrived at breathtaking stagings that remain brilliant in the memories of those who were able to see them.

'Theatre in the Round' was favoured by actors because there was no scenery to distract the attention of the audience from their performance. It also seemed like a return to Shakespeare's own intention that the words alone presented the setting. The main problem with this type of staging was that an actor could not remain in any one position for long, for fear of annoying the section of his audience to whom his back was turned or whose view he was blocking. Performances had to be carefully choreographed to allow a constant change of position and direction that seemed perfectly natural and yet always maintained the audience's attention.

Joanne Brewster's Diary, September 1961

My visit to London started badly and I mean bad! The plane was three hours late and I had problems with my ears, real painful, made me feel sick. Then when we got into Victoria with our bags, there was no trolley for us to take it to the Underground, or the 'Tube' as they call it here, so George and I had to lug the darned trunks down the road from the coach station.

We then had to negotiate the stairs crammed with folk rushing to work. Finally got down to the platform and then had to wait a long time for a train. The good thing about this horrible episode was that on the wall I saw an arresting playbill advertising a play by Shakespeare that I had never heard of; I mean, who's heard of Measure for Measure? The play is at Saint Martin's Theatre and finishes its run this very evening. While we are here, George wants to go see The Mousetrap which I'm told has run in the same theatre for nine years. That can wait.

Whatever else I am going to do today, I am darned sure I am going to see this play. So we are going to do nothing until this evening but sleep. The hotel is not at all bad, in fact I think its cute and only a few minutes from the river Thames and Blackfriars Bridge. To sleep!

The cut-out pieces for this scene are on page 47. The instructions on how to assemble it are on page 44.

This area glues to page 41

This page becomes the base of a three-dimensional pop-up scene telling the story of a visit to St. Martin's Theatre in 1961 by Joanne Brewster, an American visitor to London and her husband. To create it:

1. Remove page 39 completely from the book by cutting along the solid line.
2. Cut out the T-shaped piece precisely by cutting around the solid outline.
3. Score along the dotted line and fold it towards you to make a valley fold. Crease firmly to make a hinged flap.

4. Check that the top of the T fits over this grey shaded area and that the hinged flap covers the text beneath. Then glue this flap carefully into position. It then forms the backdrop for the theatre scene.
5. The remaining pieces to complete this scene are on page 45 and the detailed instructions are given on page 44.

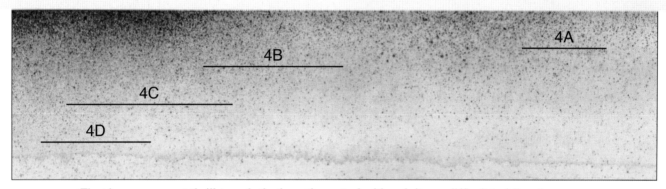

The play was a great thrill to us both, the acting superb although it was difficult to follow the English pronunciation at first. I was puzzled at the opening by the set. The curtain was already up when we took our seats and we had about ten minutes just looking at the stage. Just like the poster there was a huge pair of binoculars just staring out at us, out of the dark, nothing else.

Then two actors walked on to the set, dressed in Victorian frock coats and before they had uttered a word and to the sound of a street piano, a Victorian-style blind came down in front of the binoculars and closed off the back of the set. We were in a room of the Duke's palace. We soon settled in to the conventions set by the director and his designer. The idea of setting this story into a Victorian room with blinds that gave the illusion of privacy but through which the ever present binoculars seemed to spy, was for me a perfect metaphor for this tale of secret lust and official hypocrisy. I particularly liked the squalid back street scene with Mistress Overdone and the gentlemen. The street had been painted, very simply in black on a white Venetian blind and, in the centre was a lamp post with empty hanging baskets which could have been mistaken for the scales of justice. George muttered something about it being too clever by half, but I thought it was great. I'm off to sleep, for a week I think, but this is a precious memory.

It's now on midnight and I'm starving. We tried to eat before going to the theatre but, would you believe, no restaurant was open for dinner before we had to go to the play and when we came out of the theatre we were told we were too late to be served! That's London for you!!

Costumes of today

As in Shakespeare's time, costume plays an important part in setting the scene and telling the story. However, actors are always keenly aware of their physical imperfections and tend to feel happiest when dressed in something resembling their everyday clothes. Many a fine actor has a poor set of legs and so doublet and hose have largely given way to jerkin and trousers tucked into boots. Today, historical accuracy in costume is no longer considered essential, in fact it is sometimes greeted with derision by critics. Although countless performances are powerfully presented in modern clothes, Shakespeare's language may seem unnaturally convoluted when spoken by people in jeans and sweat shirts. Nowadays it is more usual to compromise between modern and historic styles to search for something which is comfortable for the actors and yet which defines the characters.

A new vision, a new Globe

Four hundred years of playing and four hundred years of exploration and still we seek new truths and new ways to experience the magic that Shakespeare made. So much has been gained and yet so much lost that may be found again, now that Shakespeare's Globe stands, once more, on the south bank of the Thames. Sam Wannamaker's Dream has come to fruition.

Shakespeare performed in and wrote for the original Globe Theatre and to see a performance on the 'New Globe's' stage is an astonishing experience for us. Until you have seen a play there, it is difficult to imagine the natural directness of contact between audience and actors and between members of the audience themselves.

I approached the production of **Two Gentlemen of Verona** when it was performed at the Globe in 1996 with some scepticism. There was the excitement of any new venture but I did not expect to really enjoy it. Curiosity about what the theatre was like was the main motivation and my heart sank a little when I realised that the comedy was to be played in modern clothes. Yes, I know that plays were often played in contemporary clothes in Shakespeare's time, but then the theatre and the language were contemporary too. It did not take long for me to realise, however, that I was experiencing a new sensation, not just witnessing the play.

The apparently free banter between the actors and the audience and the actors' ability to encourage audience participation without allowing them to break the rhythm of the play was both astonishing and, at the same time, refreshing. At the end of the play, when the applause began to die down, another surprise awaited us. As in Shakespeare's time, a lewd 'jig' was performed. All the cast were masked and mimed outrageously to bring the entertainment to a close.

A modern performance, but without lighting, without amplified sound and with an audience aware of themselves as a group who had gathered together to watch and comment on the play and the players. What a revelation!

Where do we go from here? Of course, we shall continue to rediscover and recreate these wonderful plays in new ways. The 'New Globe' will not become the only way or indeed the right way to present the plays. We have a richness of experience and technical possibilities that Shakespeare could never have dreamt of. As we have seen through the four pop-up theatre scenes, the experience of a visit to the theatre was different at different times and to different people.

Shakespeare on Stage will continue and will evolve, of that we are sure. What it will evolve into, only the future will reveal.

Our revels now are ended. These our actors,
As I foretold you, were all spirits and
Are melted into air; into thin air;
And like the baseless fabric of this vision,
The cloud-capped towers, the gorgeous palaces,
The solemn temples, the great globe itself,
Yea, all which it inherit, shall dissolve
And, like this insubstantial pageant faded,
Leave not a rack behind.

The Tempest act 4 scene 1

How to Make each Stand-up Scene

1. Glue the backdrop into position as described on the page for that scene.

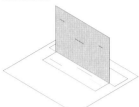

2. Cut out the tableau and bridge pieces from pages 45 or 47 which have the relevant scene number, keeping well away from the outlines.

3. Score along the dotted lines and then cut out each piece precisely.

4. Glue each tableau piece to the base so that its front edge lines up exactly with the printed black line on the base, working in alphabetical order.

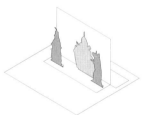

5. Continue in alphabetical order, glueing each bridge piece in position so that the colour faces upwards and the top edge lines up with the printed black line on the backdrop or tableau piece.

6. Spread glue on the flaps of the bridges marked with a ✤ and then glue them to the back of the tableau pieces so that the bridge is parallel to the base.

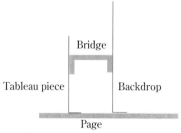

The bridge must be parallel to the base

7. After glueing each bridge into position, close the flap carefully and press it down in order to check that everything folds away flat.

8. When all four scenes are completed, you might care to glue a rectangle of white paper over these instructions.

2A

1A

1B

2C

2D

2B

1F

1C

1E

1D

3D

3C

4D

3B

3A

4H

4C

FOR
SALE

4B

4A

4E

4F

4G

4H